TRAVELS WITH MAX

HOW A BILL BECOMES A LAW

From Your Community
To Washington, D.C.

EXECUTIVE BRANCH

JUDICIAL BRANCH

LEGISLATIVE BRANCH

MAX

Educational Activities
Fun for Ages 6-12
A Resource Book

Illustrated by Kari Zwick
Produced by MAX's Publications

Regarding permission to reproduce any parts
of the book, call 1-800-4-MAX-008 or e-mail
MAX's Publications at max@maxbooks.com.

ISBN: 1-888575-11-5

Printed in the United States of America

KIDS, PARENTS & TEACHERS

Welcome to *Travels with MAX: How a Bill Becomes a Law—From Your Community to Washington, D.C.*

This book reinforces the philosophy that fun is learning and learning is fun. Puzzles, mazes, brain teasers and MAX's Facts help children to understand the basic concepts of American government.

Written for elementary and middle school students, children will learn about the founding of this great nation, ways they can take an active role in their local, state and federal government, and how a bill becomes a law from the local to the federal level. To learn more about the legislative process, Web sites for the Senate and the House are listed on page 42.

The authors would like to thank the helpful people who work in the Office of the Secretary of the United States Senate for their support and assistance in preparing this book.

The authors would also like to thank the following teachers of the Lima, Ohio, school system for their help in proofreading and editing this book: Kathleen Walker, Perry Landin and Edward Hoffmeyer.

MAX's Publications writes and publishes children's books about historic places and famous people. To learn more about MAX's books, please call our toll-free number at **1-800-4-MAX-008** or visit our book Web site at **www.maxbooks.com**.

Thank you for traveling with us,

Nancy Ann Van Wie

Nancy Ann Van Wie, M.Ed., and MAX
Authors

MAX'S WASHINGTON, D.C. BOOKS

The following books, written about Washington, D.C.,
are also available from MAX's Publications:

Travels with MAX to the U.S. Capitol Building
Travels with MAX to the White House
Travels with MAX to the Supreme Court
Travels with MAX to Washington, D.C.
Mystery at the White House: A President is Missing!

Kids and teachers are reading my books. To learn more about my fun and educational travel activity *and* mystery chapter books, check out my Web site on the Internet at **www.maxbooks.com**. Here's where you can also play games, laugh at silly riddles, and learn fun facts. Mate, be sure to tell your teachers and friends about my Web site.

CONTENTS

TRAVELS WITH MAX

Good Day, Mate. My name is MAX.

I am a well-known author and a **V.I.K**. (Very Important Koala). I travel around the world visiting famous places and meeting important people.

Today we are going to travel to Washington, D.C.—the capital of the United States—to learn how a bill becomes a law. On our journey, we will learn about the brave people who founded this great nation, the rights and freedoms American citizens enjoy, and how you and your friends can make a difference by becoming involved in your community, state and federal government.

There are puzzles and mazes
to solve, MAX's Facts to learn,
and brain teasers to answer.

Are you ready to have fun?
Then follow me, Mate!

LONG AGO

Over 500 years ago, an Italian seaman named Christopher Columbus believed he could reach the continent of Asia by sailing west from Europe across the Atlantic Ocean.

In August 1492, Columbus and his crew of 90 men left Spain with three ships—the Nina, the Pinta and the Santa Maria.

On October 12, 1492, Columbus spotted land. It was an island in the Caribbean (kar-e-be-en) Sea. The people he met ate foods he had never eaten, such as corn, and they smoked a strange plant called tobacco. The people he met were Native Americans. Columbus had found a continent that Europeans did not know existed. It was the continent of North America.

Can you find the 8 hidden objects below that Christopher Columbus might have seen while crossing the Atlantic Ocean?

cup   pencil   knife   heart   star   letter B   apple   scissors

THE 13 COLONIES

After Christopher Columbus found North America, people from European countries sailed across the Atlantic Ocean to claim land there. One of the European countries to claim land in North America was England.

As the English arrived in North America, they began setting up **colonies** along the eastern coast. A colony is a settlement ruled by another country. The first permanent English settlement in America was Jamestown, Virginia. It was founded in 1607. The colonists named it Jamestown in honor of their king, King James I. By the 1700s, 13 English colonies were established.

Below are the 13 original colonies.

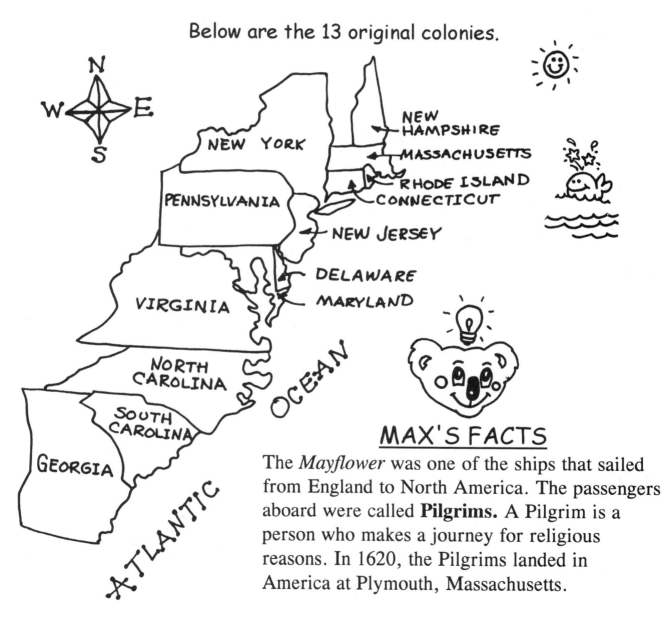

MAX'S FACTS

The *Mayflower* was one of the ships that sailed from England to North America. The passengers aboard were called **Pilgrims.** A Pilgrim is a person who makes a journey for religious reasons. In 1620, the Pilgrims landed in America at Plymouth, Massachusetts.

THE AMERICAN REVOLUTION

For over 100 years, the 13 colonies had to pay taxes to their English rulers. In 1763 when King George III demanded more taxes, the colonists decided they no longer wanted to be ruled by England. They wanted to be independent and free. The colonists decided to **rebel** (to rise in arms against a country or ruler). In 1775 war broke out between the 13 colonies and England. It was the start of the American Revolution.

Can you find the 10 words below hidden in my War Puzzle?
Look up, down and across. Good luck, Mate!

FREEDOM   TAXES   KING

AMERICA   REBEL   RULE

COLONY

FIGHT

WAR

NO

R	X	F	I	G	H	T
B	S	R	E	B	E	L
T	P	E	K	I	N	G
A	M	E	R	I	C	A
X	N	D	U	N	X	W
E	C	O	L	O	N	Y
S	K	M	E	W	A	R

A NATION IS BORN

In 1776, one year after the American Revolution began, colonial **delegates** (people chosen to act for others) met in Philadelphia, Pennsylvania, to decide how the colonies should deal with England.

The delegates decided that the 13 colonies should become free and independent of England. Thomas Jefferson of Virginia wrote the statement explaining the decision. The statement is known as the Declaration of Independence. The delegates signed the Declaration of Independence on July 4, 1776. On that day the United States of America was born!

DECLARATION OF INDEPENDENCE
(2nd paragraph)

We hold these truths to be self-evident, that all men are created equal, that they are endowed by their Creator with certain unalienable rights, that among these are life, liberty, and the pursuit of happiness.

**Below are 6 words taken from the Declaration of Independence.
Can you put the words in alphabetical order?**

LIBERTY   HAPPINES   EQUAL   RIGHTS   CREATED   LIFE

1. _____   2. _____

3. _____   4. _____

5. _____   6. _____

AMERICANS WIN THE WAR

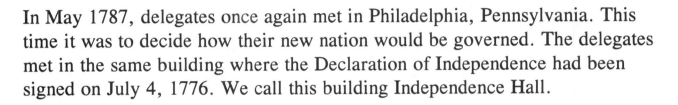

In 1783 the Americans won the Revolutionary War. Finally, they were independent and free of English rule.

Now, as a new nation, the 13 states agreed that the United States of America needed a new plan of government.

In May 1787, delegates once again met in Philadelphia, Pennsylvania. This time it was to decide how their new nation would be governed. The delegates met in the same building where the Declaration of Independence had been signed on July 4, 1776. We call this building Independence Hall.

Can you help the delegate find his way to Philadelphia?

THE U.S. CONSTITUTION

When the delegates arrived in Philadelphia, they had an important job to do. They were about to write a **constitution** (a plan of government).

The first thing the delegates did was to choose George Washington, a delegate from Virginia, as head of the meeting. The next thing was to begin planning a government with three branches, or parts.

The delegates agreed they did not want their country ruled by one person, such as a king. They wanted what they called separation of powers and checks and balances. So the Constitution provided for three branches of government: the **legislative** (lej-is-la-tiv) branch, **executive** (eg-zek-u-tiv) branch and **judicial** (ju-dish-el) branch. Each branch could check on one another, and no one branch could have too much power.

THREE BRANCHES OF GOVERNMENT

The first three articles, or parts, of the United States Constitution are about the three branches of government.

ARTICLE I: LEGISLATIVE BRANCH

The legislative branch is represented by **Congress**. Congress is made up of two houses, the Senate and the House of Representatives. Congress makes laws; collects taxes and borrows money; prints and coins money; and provides for and maintains the armed forces.

ARTICLE II: EXECUTIVE BRANCH

The executive branch is represented by the **President** of the United States. The President carries out the laws that Congress makes. The President also heads the armed forces; makes treaties; and signs or vetoes laws.

ARTICLE III: JUDICIAL BRANCH

The judicial branch is represented by the **Supreme Court**. The Supreme Court explains the laws and decides if laws passed by Congress are in keeping with the Constitution—the supreme law of the land.

THE LEGISLATIVE BRANCH

Article I of the Constitution, which sets up the legislative branch (Congress), states the qualifications (kwal-uh-fuh-kay-shuns) needed to serve as a **Member of Congress.**

The House of Representatives

To serve as a Representative, you must:

- be at least 25 years old.
- be a U.S. citizen for at least seven years.
- live in the state that you wish to represent.

If elected, you will serve two years.

The Senate

To serve as a Senator, you must:

- be at least 30 years old.
- be a U.S. citizen for at least nine years.
- live in the state that you wish to represent.

If elected, you will serve six years.

Can you find the 10 words below hidden in my Congress puzzle?

LAW   SENATE   HOUSES

STATE   ELECT   CONGRESS

VOTE   SERVE

HOUSE

BILL

X	H	O	U	S	E	P	W
C	O	N	G	R	E	S	S
V	U	B	I	L	L	E	T
O	S	F	X	A	E	R	A
T	E	Q	P	W	C	V	T
E	S	E	N	A	T	E	E

THE EXECUTIVE BRANCH

Article II of the Constitution, which sets up the executive branch (headed by the President), states the qualifications needed to serve as President.

To become President of the United States, a person must:

- be at least 35 years old.
- be a natural born citizen of the U.S.
- have lived in the U.S. for 14 years before the election.

If elected, the President will hold office for a **term** (a period of time) of four years, together with a vice president who is chosen for the same term.

How many different words can you make from the word PRESIDENT?

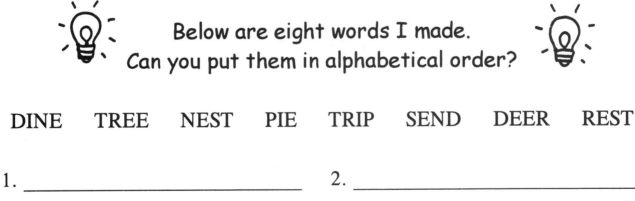

Below are eight words I made. Can you put them in alphabetical order?

DINE   TREE   NEST   PIE   TRIP   SEND   DEER   REST

1. _____   2. _____

3. _____   4. _____

5. _____   6. _____

7. _____   8. _____

THE JUDICIAL BRANCH

Article III of the Constitution sets up the judicial branch of the United States government, which is represented by the Supreme Court.

The Supreme Court is made up of nine judges called **justices**. There are eight associate justices and one chief justice. They are chosen by the President, but must be approved by the Senate. The justices serve for life or until they retire.

The first Chief Justice of the Supreme Court was appointed in 1789.
Who was he? To find out, do the following:

A) Spell the missing words by putting the correct letters in the spaces. B) Use those same letters to fill in the spaces at the bottom that have matching numbers.

1. The judicial __ __ __ __ __ __ is represented __ __ the Supreme Court.
          1 2 3 4 5 6   7 8

2. The Supreme Court is made up __ __ nine __ __ __ __ __ __ .
           9 10   11 12 13 14 15 16

3. The nine judges are called __ __ __ __ __ __ __ __ .
        17 18 19 20 21 22 23 24

    The first Chief Justice was __ __ __ __ __ __ __ .
            17 9 6 4   11 3 8

11   Answer: John Jay

THE CONSTITUTION IS LAW

On September 17, 1787, the delegates signed the Constitution. However, before it could become the nation's law, 9 of the 13 states had to **ratify** (approve) the Constitution. On June 21, 1788, New Hampshire was the ninth state to ratify it. On that day the U.S. Constitution became the law of the land.

Below is the **preamble** (introduction) to the Constitution.

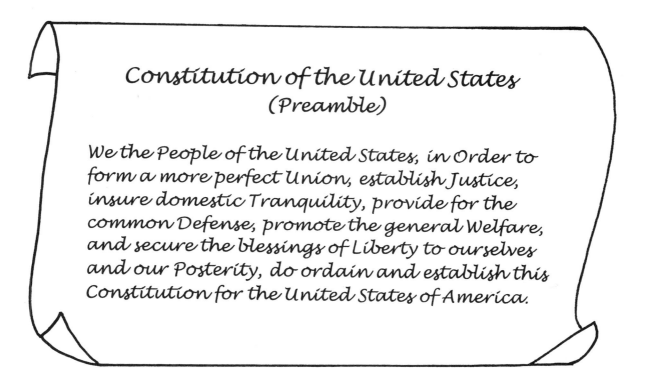

Constitution of the United States
(Preamble)

We the People of the United States, in Order to form a more perfect Union, establish Justice, insure domestic Tranquility, provide for the common Defense, promote the general Welfare, and secure the blessings of Liberty to ourselves and our Posterity, do ordain and establish this Constitution for the United States of America.

Do you know who was the first delegate to sign the Constitution?

To find out, circle the capital letters and write them on the spaces below.

niGmEagOpnRvcGetEwhgWaAplmSvHuIoNqGmTlkOmN

_ _ _ _ _ _ _ _ _   _ _ _ _ _ _ _ _ _ _

Answer: George Washington

NO BILL OF RIGHTS

After Americans read the Constitution, many were upset to learn that it did not include a bill of rights. A bill of rights guarantees citizens certain basic rights.

One basic right Americans wanted was the freedom to worship as they pleased. In England, people were not allowed this right. The Church of England was the official church. People who chose a different church were often punished.

To add a bill of rights to the Constitution would mean changing it. Would that be possible? Yes, the delegates had set up the Constitution so **amendments** (additions to the Constitution) could be made. Before an amendment can be added to the Constitution it has to be approved by two-thirds of the Senate and the House of Representatives. Then three-fourths of the states must ratify it.

Another freedom Americans wanted in a bill of rights was the freedom of ...

To find out the answer, do the following:

A. Solve the math problems.

45	95	81	74	53
+32	+11	+44	+88	+19
W	S	B	P	E

B. Circle the letters with the even-numbered (2, 4, etc.) math answers.

45	87	91	63	73
- 20	- 59	- 44	- 57	-11
K	E	A	C	H

C. Starting with the first circled letter, fill in the blanks with the circled letters to spell the name of the freedom.

The answers is: Freedom of ___ ___ ___ ___ ___ ___

Answer: ɥɔǝǝdS

YES, A BILL OF RIGHTS

Government leaders agreed with the people that a bill of rights should be added to the Constitution. In 1791 the first 10 amendments, called the Bill of Rights, were added. These basic rights are guaranteed to all Americans.

AMENDMENT 1

Freedom of religion.

Freedom of speech.

Freedom of press.

Freedom of assembly.

AMENDMENT 2

The right to keep arms.

AMENDMENT 3

Quartering of soldiers.

AMENDMENT 4

Searches and seizures.

AMENDMENT 5

Rights of accused persons.

AMENDMENT 6

Criminal cases-rights to a speedy trial.

AMENDMENT 7

Jury trial in civil cases.

AMENDENT 8

No excessive bail or punishment allowed.

AMENDMENT 9

Other rights of the people not listed in the Constitution.

AMENDMENT 10

Power of the states and the people.

THE FIRST PRESIDENT

Now that the United States had a new plan of government, the Constitution, it was time to elect its first President.

On April 30, 1789, on the balcony of Federal Hall in New York City, George Washington placed his right hand on the Bible and repeated the **oath** (promise) of office to become the first President of the United States.

The words he repeated are: "I do solemnly swear that I will faithfully execute the office of President of the United States, and will to the best of my ability, preserve, protect and defend the Constitution of the United States."

To help President Washington run the government, Congress passed laws that set up the President's **Cabinet**.

A Cabinet is a group of government officials who head government departments and give advice to the President. Most of the Cabinet members are called Secretaries. A President nominates his own Cabinet members, but his choices must be approved by the Senate.

MAX'S FACTS

President Washington's Cabinet was made up of five positions: the Secretary of Treasury, Secretary of State, Secretary of War, Postmaster General, and Attorney General. Today the President's Cabinet is made up of 14 positions: the Attorney General and 13 Secretaries, which includes the Secretary of Education.

THE NATION'S CAPITAL

Now that the United States had its first President, people wanted to know where he would live. Congress decided that the nation's capital, where the President would live, would be located between the states of Virginia and Maryland. President Washington chose a site along the Potomac (puh-toe-mik) River. The site was not part of any state. It was a district, or an area set aside for a special purpose. It was named Washington, District of Columbia.

President Washington hired a French-born architect named Pierre (pyair) L'Enfant (lahn-fhan) to design a beautiful and well-planned city. L'Enfant mapped out where streets and parks would be. Then he showed President Washington where he thought the three branches of government (legislative branch, executive branch, and judicial branch) should be located.

In the middle of the city, on a hilltop where everyone could see it, is where L'Enfant said the legislative branch (Congress) should be located. President Washington agreed. This is where the **Capitol** Building would be built.

MAX'S FACTS

Did you know the capital of the United States was named Washington, D.C., in honor of President Washington and Christopher Columbus?

MAX'S FACTS

Capital (spelled with an a) is the seat of government for a state or nation. **Capitol** (spelled with an o) is the building where lawmakers meet.

THE U.S. CAPITOL BUILDING

The U.S. Capitol Building was designed by William Thornton in 1792. The first section of it was ready for Congress in 1800. Over the next several years, some changes were made to Mr. Thornton's design. One change was the adding of a cast-iron **dome** (rounded roof) that weighs nine million pounds!

Another change took place when the Statue of Freedom was placed on top of the Capitol dome in 1863. This awesome-looking bronze statue stands 19 1/2 feet tall (as tall as a giraffe) and weighs over 15,000 pounds (more than an elephant weighs)!

To see an enlarged picture of the Statue of Freedom and learn more interesting facts, turn the page, Mate.

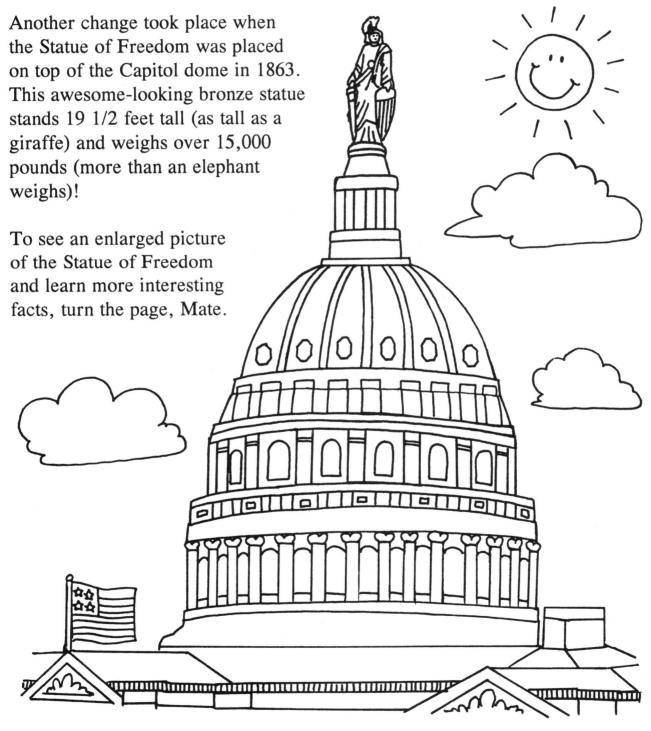

THE STATUE OF FREEDOM

The Statue of Freedom is sculptured in the form of a woman. On her head is a helmet in the shape of an eagle's head (the eagle is the national bird of the United States). On the middle of her dress is a round pin with the letters "US," which stand for the United States.

In her right hand rests a sword, which represents the military force of this nation. In her left hand is a wreath. It represents peace and victory. Underneath the wreath is the shield of the United States with 13 stripes. The 13 stripes represent the first 13 states.

On the bottom of the Statue of Freedom are the Latin words: E Pluribus Unum," which mean "Out of Many [States], One [Nation]."

In 1993, 130 years after the Statue was placed on top of the Capitol dome, the U. S. Capitol Preservation Commission provided money to have the Statue of Freedom **restored** (brought back to its original condition). It was necessary to restore the Statue because the bronze was corroding and there was a crack in the pedestal.

E PLURIBUS UNUM

On May 9, 1993, a helicopter lifted the Statue off the dome and placed it in a parking lot next to the Capitol Building. Here is where it was cleaned and repaired. After six months' work, when the Statue of Freedom was looking as good as new, a helicopter returned the Statue to its pedestal on the top of the Capitol dome.

MORE CAPITOL CHANGES

As the United States of America grew, so did the Capitol Building.

Today the Capitol Building has two wings and a middle section. The Capitol does not have a back and a front. It has a West Front and an East Front.

The U.S. Capitol is one of the most famous buildings in the world. It is a symbol of this great nation's government. Here is where Congress meets to pass laws that affect the lives of all Americans.

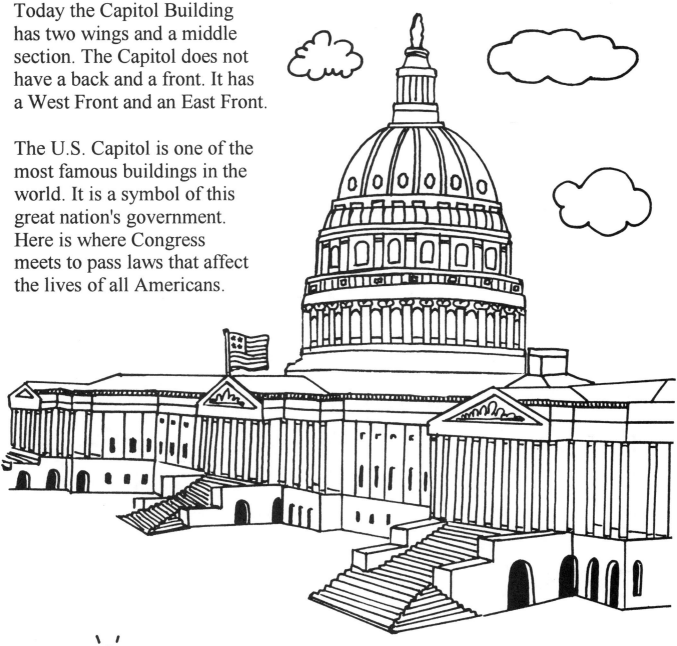

MAX'S FACTS
Did you know the Capitol Building has 540 rooms, 658 windows (108 in the dome alone), approximately 850 doorways, and is about the length of two football fields?

THE WHITE HOUSE

In 1792, the same year that the U.S. Capitol Building was designed, James Hoban, an architect (ar-ke-tekt), began building the White House. In 1800, when it was ready for the President, George Washington was no longer in office. Johns Adams, the second President of the United States, was the first President to live in the White House.

MAX'S FACTS

Did you know the White House was first called the President's House? It was built of gray sandstone and white paint was used to waterproof it. Over the years so many coats of white paint were applied, people started calling it the White House. In 1901, 101 years after John Adams moved into the President's House, it was officially renamed the White House.

20

THE U.S SUPREME COURT

By 1800 Congress was meeting in the Capitol Building and the President was living in the White House, but where was the Supreme Court located? From 1800 to 1935 the Supreme Court was located in several rooms throughout the Capitol Building. In 1935 a separate building was built for the Supreme Court.

The Supreme Court building looks like a Greek temple. Atop its 36 steps are 16 marble columns. Above them are the words **"Equal Justice Under Law."** These words express the responsibility of the Supreme Court, which is to interpret the law fairly according to the Constitution of the United States.

As you walk up the steps there are two huge statues to the left and to the right. The female statue on the left represents the Contemplation of Justice. The male statue on the right represents the Authority of Law.

21

MAX'S
BRAIN  TEASERS

Okay, Mate, it's time to test your brain power. These questions are hard, so put on your thinking cap. Circle the answer you think is correct, then turn to the page listed to learn how you did. No peeking allowed! Good luck.

1. Christopher Columbus discovered the continent of:
   Asia   OR   Australia   OR   North America   (Page 2)

2. The English colonies were ruled by which country?
   United States   OR   England   OR   Spain   (Page 4)

3. Who wrote the Declaration of Independence?
   Thomas Jefferson   OR   George Washington   (Page 5)

4. The legislative branch of government is represented by the:
   Supreme Court   OR   President   OR   Congress   (Page 8)

5. The Bill of Rights is part of which famous document?
   U.S. Constitution   OR   Declaration of Independence   (Page 14)

6. The nation's capital is located between the states of:
   California and Texas   OR   Maryland and Virginia   (Page 16)

7. The famous bronze statue on top of the Capitol dome is the:
   Statue of Freedom   OR   Statue of Liberty   (Page 17)

8. Who was the first President to live in the White House?
   Thomas Jefferson OR George Washington OR John Adams (Page 20)

THE UNITED STATES, TODAY!

When the United States of America was founded there were 13 states.
Today there are 50!

Can you find your state on the map?

Write the name of your state. _____

Find the star on the map.

This is where Washington, D.C., the capital of the United States, is located.

MAX'S FACTS

Did you know that Washington, DC (D.C. stands for District of Columbia) is the only city or town in America that is **not** part of a state?

COMMUNITY GOVERNMENT

Each state has cities and towns. People call their city or town a community.

What is the name of your community?

_____

Every community forms a government. A government makes rules for the people in the community. These rules are called laws. People who live in a community are required to obey the laws.

Name two laws of your community.

1. _____

2. _____

Do you have an idea that should be a law of your community?

_____

The mayor is usually the head of a community's government and is elected by the **citizens** who live in the community. A citizen is a person who is born in a country or who has earned the right to become a member of the country by law.

Can you name four other community leaders that citizens might elect?

1. _____   2. _____

3. _____   4. _____

GOOD CITIZENS

Community leaders listen to what the citizens say. They work with the citizens to try to make their community a better place to live.

Every member of a community can make a difference, including children. If you have an idea that could improve your community, write to your mayor.

WRITE TODAY ▷ WRITE TO YOUR MAYOR

Mayor's name: _____

Mayor's address: _____

_____

_____

Good citizens obey the laws and take an interest in their government. Can you find the 13 words hidden in my Citizen Puzzle?

VOTE CITZEN RIGHTS

OBEY CHANGE VOICE

IDEA ELECT WRITE

GOOD WORK

FREEDOM

LAWS

A	Z	V	O	I	C	E	F
X	R	O	B	E	Y	K	R
C	I	T	I	Z	E	N	E
H	G	E	L	E	C	T	E
A	H	I	A	G	O	O	D
N	T	D	W	O	R	K	O
G	S	E	S	X	L	B	M
E	V	A	W	R	I	T	E

THE RIGHT TO VOTE

Community leaders are **elected** by the citizens of the community. To elect means to choose by voting. Before a person may vote, he or she must be an American citizen and at least 18 years old.

How many more years will it be before you can vote?

18   (voting age)

- ___   (your age)

_____

(more years)

Voting is very special. There are people in other parts of the world who do not have the freedom to vote as Americans do. Voting is fun, too! You go behind a curtain to vote secretly.

When citizens vote, they are voting for a **candidate's** political party. A candidate is a person who seeks or is nominated for an office.

The two main political parties are Democrats and Republicans. The symbol of the Democratic Party is the donkey. The symbol of the Republican Party is the elephant.

_____   _____
DEMOCRAT   REPUBLICAN

STATE GOVERNMENT

The community government works with the state government. The state government provides services to all the people of the state.

The state government, like the federal government, is divided into three branches: the legislative branch (makes the laws), the executive branch (carries out the laws), the judicial branch (makes sure the laws are obeyed).

The governor is the head of the executive branch.

Who is the governor of your state? _____

Is your governor a Democrat or Republican? _____

The governor and the **legislators** (lawmakers) are elected by the voters of the state. The governor and the legislators meet at the state capitol building. The city in which this building is located is the capital of the state.

What city is the capital of your state? _____

 Your legislators and governor are interested in hearing from you. Do you have an idea that could make your state a better place to live?

Unscramble the letters below to spell the names of three states.

1. Honolulu is the capital of _____
   AIWAHI

2. Juneau is the capital of _____
   LAKASA

3. Sacramento is the capital of _____
   CIALFONIRA

Answers: **Hawaii, Alaska, California**

FEDERAL GOVERNMENT

America's government is called the federal or national government. It provides services to all the people of the United States. One state cannot plan and make laws for another, so citizens from each state elect people to **represent** them on a federal level. To represent means to speak or act for a person or a group of people.

In 1863 after the Battle of Gettysburg, President Abraham Lincoln, the 16th President of the United States, gave a famous speech called the Gettysburg Address.

In that speech President Lincoln said the United States had a "government of the people, by the people, for the people."

What did President Lincoln mean when he said those words?

A government that is "of the people, by the people, for the people," is when all the citizens are part of government. This form of government is called a **democracy**. A democracy means power is shared by all the citizens.

 During what war did President Lincoln deliver the Gettysburg Address?

To find out, circle the capital letters and write them on the spaces below.

mjTkiHabjsoEhgtrCnIwalkfVnepzxIrtLdkvWmbuAglpRxw

— — — — — — — — — — — — — — — — —

Answer: The Civil War

CONGRESS

The people that voters of each state elect to represent them on a federal level are the Members of Congress. There are 535 men and women who serve as the Members of Congress (100 Senators and 435 Representatives). Congress meets in the U.S. Capitol Building.

On page eight you learned that Congress, the lawmaking body of the United States government, is made up of two houses: the House of Representatives and the Senate. The House of Representatives meets in the House Chamber and the Senate meets in the Senate Chamber. When the Senate or the House of Representatives is in **session** (a meeting), you can watch them work.

MAX'S FACTS

Whenever the Senate or House is in session, a flag flies over its chamber. At night, a lantern in the dome is lit when either is in session.

THE HOUSE OF REPRESENTATIVES

On page nine you learned the qualifications that are needed to serve as a Representative. Representatives are elected by the people of their state.

The House of Representatives is made up of 435 members elected every two years from 50 states. The number of Representatives a state has depends on its **population** (how many people live in an area). To find out how many people live in each state, the government takes a count of the population every ten years. This count is called a **census**. It is the law that the census must be taken. It is stated in Article I of the Constitution. Since 1790, when George Washington was President, a census has been taken every ten years.

After each census the states redraw the lines of their congressional **districts**. A district is a territory marked off for political purposes. Each district is made up of approximately 600,000 people. Each district is represented by one House member.

Name the Representative that serves your district. _____

How many Representatives does your state elect? _____

Follow the clues to learn which state elects the most Representatives.

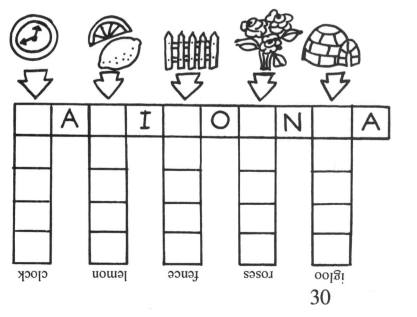

	A		I		O		N		A

clock   lemon   fence   roses   igloo

30

Answer: California

THE HOUSE CHAMBER

Welcome to the House Chamber. Here is where the 435 members of the House of Representatives meet. The House Chamber is one of the world's largest legislative (lawmaking) rooms.

At the front of the room sits the leader, the Speaker of the House.

Who is the Speaker of the House? _____

Is the Speaker of the House a Democrat or Republican? _____

To the Speaker's right sit the Democrats; to his left sit the Republicans. The Representatives sit on benches. They do not usually have assigned seats.

When the House is in session, visitors are allowed to sit in the gallery and watch the Representatives work.

THE SENATE

On page nine you learned the qualifications that are needed to serve as a Senator. Senators are elected by the people of their state. The Senate is made up of 100 members, two from each state. Each Senator is elected for a term of six years. One-third of the Senate is elected every two years.

Write the names of the two Senators who represent your state.

1. _____

2. _____

How many different words can you make from the word SENATOR?
I made six. Can you put them in alphabetical order?

SNORE   ANTS   SEAT   EAT   TORE   NEAT

1. _____   2. _____

3. _____   4. _____

5. _____   6. _____

MAX'S FACTS

One Senator who went on to become President is John F. Kennedy. He served as Senator from the state of Massachusetts from 1953 to 1960. In 1961 he became the 35th U.S. President. At the age of forty-four, he was the youngest man elected President. In 1963 President Kennedy was killed by an assassin's bullet. At the age of forty-six, he was the youngest President to die.

THE SENATE CHAMBER

Welcome to the Senate Chamber. At the front of this room sits the Vice President of the United States. The Vice President serves as the President of the Senate.

Who is the Vice President of the United States? _____

Is the Vice President a Democrat or Republican? _____

To the Vice President's right sit the Democrats; to his left sit the Republicans. The 100 Members of the Senate sit at assigned desks. Many of the desks are the same desks that were used by Senators in the 1800s.

In the gallery, around each wall, you will see marble busts of the former Vice Presidents of the United States. When the Senate is in session, visitors may sit in the gallery and watch the Senators work.

33

POWERS & DUTIES OF CONGRESS

Congress has many powers. Some include the power to coin money, set up the Postal Service, and declare war.

COIN MONEY **POSTAL SERVICE** **DECLARE WAR**

Members of Congress are busy people.

Members of Congress have many duties to perform, such as:

- introduce and pass new laws.

- represent their state in Congress to the best of their ability.

- meet with people from their state to listen to and discuss their ideas and concerns.

- meet with school children to talk about government and how it works.

SPECIAL TEENAGERS

To help the busy Members of Congress with their work, Congress hires teenage boys and girls called Congressional (kan-gresh-en-el) Pages. Each year Senators may **appoint** (choose) as many as 30 Pages for the Senate, and Representatives may appoint as many as 66 Pages for the House.

Pages work very hard. During the school year they attend a special school that starts early in the morning. When classes end for the day, Pages report to the office of the Senator or Representative for whom they are working.

Pages have many duties, such as delivering packages and messages. While performing their duties they learn a lot about how the American government works.

To be selected as a Page is an honor. They serve from a few months to a year. If you want to be a Page, discuss this with your parents and teachers.

Can you find the 10 words below hidden in my Page Puzzle?

BOYS   HOUSE   CLASSES

WORK   STUDY   CAPITOL

GIRLS   PAGES

APPOINT

SENATE

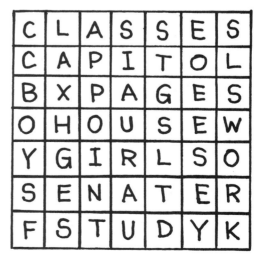

C	L	A	S	S	E	S
C	A	P	I	T	O	L
B	X	P	A	G	E	S
O	H	O	U	S	E	W
Y	G	I	R	L	S	O
S	E	N	A	T	E	R
F	S	T	U	D	Y	K

AN IDEA FOR A LAW

Congress makes laws. A law starts with an idea called a **bill**. Anyone can suggest an idea for a law, but only Congress can turn that idea into a law. Many bills that are introduced into Congress are ideas sent to the Members of Congress by businesspeople, parents, grandparents, and even children.

Write an idea that you think should become a law.

_____

Below is my idea for a law. To finish the sentence, circle the
capital letters and write them on the spaces below.
I think that every American should . . .

biRzmEagioApnzDvcMetwhgYaypmBvOutfOqmlKmSnp

— — — — — — — —   — — — — — —

36

HOW A BILL BECOMES A LAW

Okay, Mate, it's now time to learn how a bill becomes a law. Each year thousands of bills are introduced into Congress, but not all bills become laws.

Follow my 7 easy steps to learn how a bill becomes a law.

1. BILL IS INTRODUCED

A bill is introduced into the Senate or the House of Representatives by a Member of Congress, then it is sent to a committee to review the subject. All bills are numbered. "H.R." represents a House bill and "S." a Senate bill.

2. COMMITTEE CONSIDERS THE BILL

The committee reviews the bill carefully and decides if it should be chosen for further study. Usually, it is sent to a subcommittee for hearings.

HOW A BILL BECOMES A LAW

3. HEARINGS HELD

The committee holds **hearings** (meetings in which people are asked to express their ideas) so it can learn more about the bill. Sometimes the committee will consult people from the executive branch, such as experts on the subject to find out what they think. Depending on what was said at the hearings, the committee may "mark up" (rewrite) the bill.

4. DEBATE AND REFER THE BILL

After the hearings, the committee returns the bill to the chamber where it started (either in the House or Senate). When that chamber's leaders decide to **call up** (bring the bill onto the floor), members **debate** (discuss the reasons for and against) the bill, change or amend it, and vote by either passing or rejecting it.

THE HOUSE

After a bill is passed by one chamber, it is referred to the other chamber where it usually follows the same route through committee and floor action. This chamber may approve the bill as received, reject it, ignore it, or change it.

THE SENATE

HOW A BILL BECOMES A LAW

5. CONFERENCE COMMITTEE

If a bill passes in both Houses but there is a difference between the bill passed in the Senate and the billed passed in the House, a conference committee is formed. The conference committee, made up of Members of Congress from both Houses, works together to solve the difference and rewrite the bill.

6. MEMBERS VOTE

After the bill has been rewritten, both Houses vote. A "yes" vote passes the bill. A "no" vote rejects the bill. When both Houses pass the bill in identical form, then it is sent to the President for approval.

HOW A BILL BECOMES A LAW

7. THE PRESIDENT DECIDES

THE PRESIDENT APPROVES THE BILL

If the President approves the bill he signs the bill into law.

THE PRESIDENT VETOES THE BILL

If the President **vetoes** (rejects) the bill, then the bill is sent back to Congress. If both Houses pass it by a two-thirds vote, the bill becomes a law.

THE PRESIDENT DOES NOT SIGN OR VETO THE BILL

If the President does not sign or veto the bill within ten days, the bill becomes a law without the President's signature. However, if Congress is not in session those ten days, the bill fails to become a law.

MAX'S
BRAIN  TEASERS

Okay, Mate, it's that time again: time to test your brain power. These questions are difficult so be sure to *THINK* before you answer. Circle your answer, then turn to the page listed to learn how you did. No peeking allowed! Good luck.

1. Which animal is the symbol of the Democratic Party?
   Koala   OR   Donkey   OR   Kangaroo   (Page 26)

2. Which animal is the symbol of the Republican Party?
   Elephant   OR   Bald Eagle   OR   Giraffe   (Page 26)

3. The head of state government is the:
   Mayor   OR   Governor   OR   President   (Page 27)

4. How many men and women serve as Members of Congress?
   100   OR   535   OR   1,000   (Page 29)

5. How many Senators may each state elect?
   100   OR   As many as it wants   OR   2   (Page 32)

6. The U.S. Vice President serves as the President of the:
   Senate   OR   House of Representatives   OR   Congress   (Page 33)

7. A law starts with an idea called a:
   Document   OR   Bill   OR   Constitution   (Page 36)

8. If the President vetoes a bill, he is:
   Rejecting the bill   OR   Approving the bill   (Page 40)

DEBATE A BILL IN YOUR CLASS

Mate, now that you are a whiz kid on how a bill becomes a law, I have an idea. Why don't you and your classmates conduct a **mock** (pretend) debate on how a bill becomes a law and invite a Member of Congress to watch.

Together with your teacher and classmates, think about an idea that may become a law. Divide the class into two Houses: the Senate and the House of Representatives. Then follow my 7 easy steps on how a bill becomes a law, starting on page 37. Have fun, Mate, and please let me know if a Member of Congress visits your class. My e-mail address is: **max@maxbooks.com.**

The Members of Congress want to hear from you. To learn their names, addresses and more about Congress, check out these three Web sites: **www.senate.gov**, **www.house.gov** and **www.congresslink.org**. Good luck, Mate!

42